Mystery Mob

and the
Top Talent Contest

Roger Hurn

Illustrated by
Stik

RISING ★ STARS

Rising Stars UK Ltd.
22 Grafton Street, London W1S 4EX
www.risingstars-uk.com

The right of Roger Hurn to be identified as the author of this work
has been asserted by him in accordance with the Copyright,
Design and Patents Act 1988.

Published 2008

Cover design: Burville-Riley Partnership
Illustrator: Stik, Bill Greenhead for Illustration Ltd
Text design and typesetting: Andy Wilson
Publisher: Gill Budgell
Editor: Catherine Baker

British Library Cataloguing in Publication Data.
A CIP record for this book is available from the British Library

ISBN: 978-1-84680-429-8

Printed in the UK by CPI Bookmarque, Croydon, CR0 4TD

Mixed Sources
Product group from well-managed
forests and other controlled sources
www.fsc.org Cert no. TT-COC-002227
© 1996 Forest Stewardship Council

Contents

Meet the Mystery Mob   4

Chapter 1: Will E Winnit   7

Chapter 2: Stars in Their Eyes   13

Chapter 3: Out of Bounds   21

Chapter 4: Phone Tap   28

Chapter 5: It's a Knockout   34

Extras!

About the author   39

Top Talent Contest quiz   40

When I was a kid   42

Adi's favourite performing joke   43

How to win a talent contest   44

Five fantastic facts about
    talent contests   46

Showbiz lingo   47

Meet the Mystery Mob

Name:

Gummy

FYI: Gummy hasn't got much brain – and even fewer teeth.

Loves: Soup.

Hates: Toffee chews.

Fact: The brightest thing about him is his shirt.

Name:

Lee

FYI: If Lee was any cooler he'd be a cucumber.

Loves: Hip-hop.

Hates: Hopscotch.

Fact: He has his own designer label (which he peeled off a tin).

Name:

FYI: Rob lives in his own world – he's just visiting planet Earth.

Loves: Daydreaming.

Hates: Nightmares.

Fact: Rob always does his homework – he just forgets to write it down.

Name:

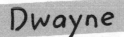

FYI: Dwayne is smarter than a tree full of owls.

Loves: Anything complicated.

Hates: Join-the-dots books.

Fact: If he was any brighter you could use him as a floodlight at football matches.

Name:

Chet

FYI: Chet is as brave as a lion with steel jaws.

Loves: Having adventures.

Hates: Knitting.

Fact: He's as tough as the chicken his granny cooks for his tea.

Name:

Adi

FYI: Adi is as happy as a football fan with tickets to the big match.

Loves: Telling jokes.

Hates: Moaning minnies.

Fact: He knows more jokes than a jumbo joke book.

1

Will E Winnit

The Mystery Mob are trying get on
Will E Winnit's top TV talent show,
Star Factor. Lee, Rob, Dwayne and
Gummy call themselves Five Aside.
They're a boy band. They perform
for Will. Lee looks cool, but Rob
can't dance, Dwayne can't sing
and Gummy keeps forgetting
the words. They're hopeless.

Will   Forget showbiz, boys. You've got
no talent. And your name
is rubbish! Five Aside? There are
only four of you in the band!
So you can't sing or dance
and you can't count either. Doh!

Lee, Rob, Dwayne and Gummy walk off.
Their dream of being a famous boy band
is over. Chet and Adi are up next.
They're doing a comedy act.

8

Adi   Hi, Mr Winnit. We're Chet
            and Adi and we're the daddies!

Chet   That's right! We're the funniest
            kids in town.

Will   Okay, guys. Go ahead and make
            me laugh. But let me warn you,
            I don't laugh at just anything.
            So you'd better be good!

Adi   That's no problem for us.

Chet   Adi knows loads of jokes.

Adi   I sure do. I've got them all
written down in my jumbo
joke book. We'd be useless
without it.

Will   Well, make sure you don't
lose it, then.

Chet   Don't you worry about that.
We won't.

Adi   Okay, Mr Winnit, pin back your
ears and get ready to chuckle.

Chet   Hey, Adi. What did you get for your birthday?

Adi   A drum. It's the best present I ever had!

Chet   Why?

Adi   'Cos my mum gives me extra pocket money every week not to play it!

Will E Winnit doesn't even crack a smile.
Adi and Chet try again.

Chet Hey, Adi, what's the best hand
to write with – left or right?

Adi Neither – it's best to write
with a pen!

Will (laughing) Okay. You guys are
so bad, you're good. You're on
the show!

2

Stars in Their Eyes

It's Saturday night and Chet and Adi
do their act in front of millions of
TV viewers. They're really bad,
and no one laughs at their jokes.

Chet   We were soooo terrible, Adi.
You should never have told
that joke about the blunt pencil.

Adi   Why not?

Chet   Because it's pointless.

Adi   Maybe you're right. I don't think
we're going to get many votes.

Chet   Oh, I'm not so sure. Perhaps
the other acts will be even
worse than us.

Adi   Hmmmm … We've got
two chances of that happening.

Chet   Really? What are they?

Adi   Fat Chance and No Chance!

The next act comes on stage.
It's Gee Wizz, the Magic Man.
He does magic tricks. He's good.

Chet   Hey, Gee Wizz does cool tricks
with his magic wand.

Adi   Yes, but I bet he thinks
he's wand-erful!

Gee Wizz is followed by Kylie the Kung Fu
Kangaroo. The audience love her.

Chet   Hey, that kangaroo's good.
I think she'll win.

Adi   Now let's not jump to
conclusions, Chet. Anyway,
it's Lotta Row the opera singer
now. She may be even better.

Lotta Row is a big lady with a big voice.

Chet   Why did she sit on top of that
ladder to sing her song?

Adi   Well, I guess she wanted to hit
the high notes. But forget her.
Here comes the last act.

Chet   It's Atomic Annie, the world's
strongest woman. They say
she can lift an elephant
with one finger.

Adi That's awesome! I've never seen a one-fingered elephant before.

Atomic Annie does her strongwoman stuff. At the end of the show, the audience votes for their favourite act. Kylie is in the lead, Gee Wizz is in second place, Atomic Annie is third, Lotta Row is fourth. Chet and Adi are a long way behind in last place.

Will   Okay, folks. The performers will
now go back to their dressing
rooms while we wait for
the TV audience to vote for
the two acts they want to see
in tonight's final! I can hardly
wait for the result!

Chet Do you think we'll get enough votes to make it to the final?

Adi It doesn't matter, Chet. Even if we do make it, we'll still lose.

Chet Why do you say that, Adi?

Adi Because someone has stolen my jumbo joke book, and without it, we're finished!

Out of Bounds

It turns out that it's not just Adi's joke book that's been stolen. Someone has taken stuff from the other acts as well.

Chet   Gee Wizz's pack of magic cards has vanished.

Adi   And he didn't even cast a spell on them.

Chet   Right! And it gets worse. Someone's put chilli pepper in Lotta Row's throat gargle!

Adi   Wow, her voice was hot stuff
before, so now her throat
really must be on fire!

Chet   You're not kidding.
After swallowing that
chilli pepper, she can only croak
like a frog. She's out of the show.

Adi   What about Atomic Annie?
Is she okay?

Chet   No way. Somebody stuck
her dumbbell to the floor
with superglue. She hurt her back
trying to lift it up,
so she's out too.

Adi   Hmmm ... it seems like we've got a weighty problem to solve here, Chet. Someone's trying to get rid of all the acts – but who?

Chet   It's not *all* the acts, Adi. Kylie the Kung Fu Kangaroo still has her black belt keeping up her Kung Fu pyjama bottoms!

Adi   Wow – now that's *very* suspicious.

The performers all crowd round Kylie.
They want to find out if she's behind
the mean tricks.

Gee Wizz Wait a minute. Kylie's got
something hidden in her pouch.
Let me see what it is.

The Magic Man puts his hand in Kylie's
pouch and pulls out a book.

Chet That's Adi's jumbo joke book!

Adi   Yes, and you don't expect to find jumbos in kangaroo pouches.

Gee Wizz So Kylie's the one behind all the bad stuff! She wants to win so much she's turned into a crook.

Will   Okay, kangaroo, hop it before I call the police.

Kylie leaves, but Will has a big problem.

Chet   Hey, now everyone else is out, we're in the final. And the only people who voted for us were our mums!

Adi   So we're going to win whatever happens, but that doesn't seem fair.

Will   It isn't. I can't have a final with only one act.

Gee Wizz Don't panic, Mr Winnit. I'm not called the Magic Man for nothing. Watch this. Hey Presto!

Gee Wizz conjures up a pack of cards
from out of thin air.

Chet   Hey, now you've got your
magic cards back you can be
in the final with us.

Adi   It'll be a play-off between
magic and jokes. And we'll win,
because our jokes are magic!

Gee Wizz We'll soon see about that, kid.
'Cos when it comes to being
funny, you two are just a joke!

Phone Tap

Chet and Adi are in their dressing room waiting to take part in the final. Something is bothering them – but it's not the fact that their act is terrible.

Adi   I don't think Kylie's to blame for stealing my joke book or doing any of that other stuff.

Chet   Why not?

Adi   Just think about it, Chet.
Whoever did those things
needed hands to do them –
not kangaroo paws.

Chet   You're right! Kylie's not guilty.
But Gee Wizz is clever with
his hands. I bet he's the one
behind all this.

Adi   Quick! Let's go and see if we can
catch him out before
the show starts.

The boys sneak up to Gee Wizz's dressing room. They can hear him giggling and talking on the phone about how he messed things up for the other acts. Luckily, Chet's got his mobile too – and he uses it to record everything Gee Wizz says.

Chet   Gotcha!

Adi   Yeah – that Gee Wizz has got
a real cheek if he reckons
he can win the contest
by framing Kylie and getting rid
of everyone else. Everyone
except us, anyway ...

Chet   I can't believe he said we're
so useless that we're no threat
to him!

Adi   Grrrr! Okay, we are useless
but he's still not going to win.
He may be the Magic Man,
but I've got a trick
up my sleeve
that'll fix him!

The boys go and tell Will E Winnit
that Gee Wizz is the bad guy.

Will   I don't believe it. You're just
         trying to get rid of Gee Wizz
         because you know he'll beat you
         in the final.

Chet   No way. I've got his confession
         on my mobile.

Adi   Play it, Chet.

Will listens to the recording in
amazement.

Will   I owe you boys an apology.
The Magic Man is a crook.
I'll kick him out of the final.

Chet   You owe Kylie an apology too,
Mr Winnit.

Adi   That's right, you do.
But don't kick Gee Wizz out.

Chet   Why not?

Adi   Because I want Mr Winnit to go
and bring Kylie back in secret.
She's going to spring a big
surprise on Gee Wizz!

It's a Knockout

It's the final. Gee Wizz does his magic trick, and the crowd clap him like mad. Then Adi and Chet walk on. Nobody claps.

Chet   Here's our last joke, everybody. Hey Adi, did you hear about Gee Wizz? He just fell down a wishing well.

Adi   Wow! So that wishing well really works!

Gee Wizz You wish! Sorry, kids, but I'm
going to win this final by a mile.

Will E Winnit steps onto the stage.
He says the votes are in and Gee Wizz
has lots more than Adi and Chet.

Gee Wizz Ha! Ha! I win!

Chet Yes, and here to give you
the prize you deserve is …

Adi   Kylie, the Kung Fu Kangaroo!

Kylie bounds on and biffs Gee Wizz
on the chin. He sits down hard on his
bottom. Will E Winnit holds Kylie's arm
up in the air.

Will   I declare Kylie is the winner
of *Star Factor* by a knockout!

The audience go wild. They clap
and cheer while Kylie chases Gee Wizz
off the stage.

Chet   Gee Wizz said our jokes weren't funny, but we had the last laugh.

Adi   Yeah. Gee Wizz called himself the Magic Man, but he ended up tragic, not magic, when Kylie made him disappear!

About the author

Roger Hurn has:

- had a hit record in Turkey
- won *The Weakest Link* on TV
- swum with sharks on the Great Barrier Reef.

Now he's a writer, and he hopes you like reading about the Mystery Mob as much as he likes writing about them.

Top Talent Contest quiz

Questions

1 How can you wow the judges by making music with your head at a Talent Contest?

2 How do you make a bandstand at a Talent Contest?

3 What kind of dancing did the rabbit do at the Talent Contest?

4 What did the space aliens sing at the Talent Contest?

5 What kind of music did the Egyptian Mummy sing at the Talent Contest?

6 Why don't balloons enter Talent Contests?

7 Why don't skeletons enter Talent Contests?

8 Why did the judges at the Talent Contest vote the bagpipe player off before he'd even started to play?

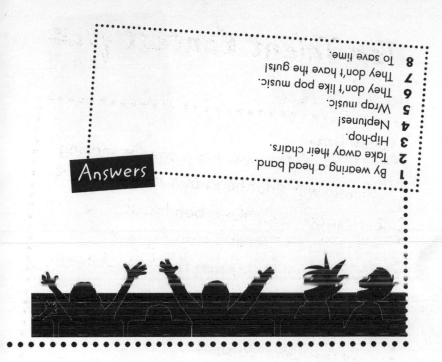

Answers

1 By wearing a head band.
2 Take away their chairs.
3 Hip-hop.
4 Neptunes!
5 Wrap music.
6 They don't like pop music.
7 They don't have the guts!
8 To save time.

How did you score?

- If you got all eight Talent Contest answers correct, then you are Top of the Pops!

- If you got six Talent Contest answers correct, then you are on your way to the top.

- If you got fewer than four Talent Contest answers correct, then you are bottom of the flops.

When I was a kid

Question When you were a kid, did you ever go on a talent show?

Roger Yes, I played elastic guitar.

Question Don't you mean you played electric guitar?

Roger No, I mean elastic guitar. I was in a rubber band!

Question Where did you learn to play music?

Roger At school. But I got locked in the music room once.

Question How come?

Roger The keys were inside the piano.

Question Do you still make music?

Roger Yes. I'm in a band with my dentist.

Question Really? What instrument does he play?

Roger A tuba toothpaste.

Adi's favourite performing joke

How can you make cool music?

Play your guitar in the fridge.

How to win a talent contest

 It always helps if you actually have some talent to begin with. If you haven't, don't let it worry you. It doesn't seem to worry most of the contestants on *American Idol*.

 It is always a good idea to practise at home before you enter a talent contest. If you're good it will help make you even better and improve your chances of winning. If you're hopeless, well, at least it won't make you any worse.

 If you're talented, ask your mum to watch your performance so she can tell you how you can improve it. If you're hopeless then just give your mum earplugs and a blindfold.

If you are completely talent free, try to persuade your dad to be one of the judges at the contest. Only tell him to do it under a false name and pretend not to know you.

 If all else fails, sneak a recording of your favourite singer inside your outfit and mime to it. If you're lucky the judges will think it really is you singing. (Be warned, this trick only works with very stupid judges.)

45

Five fantastic facts about talent contests

1 Elvis Presley lost when he entered America's biggest talent contest. He didn't need to worry; he went on to sell millions of records and became known as the King of Rock 'n' Roll.

2 The greatest band of all time, The Beatles, never won a talent contest in their lives.

3 Simon Cowell, who hosts talent contests in the UK and in the USA, is known as Mr Nasty for the unkind things he says about the contestants.

4 *Opportunity Knocks* was the first ever talent show on UK television to have viewers vote for the winners. But they didn't vote by phone or online, they had to send in a letter saying who they wanted to win.

5 A well-known actress was once beaten on a talent show by a singing dog. Maybe she was barking up the wrong tree.

Showbiz lingo

Agent A showbiz agent is someone who finds work for actors, singers, musicians and writers. This kind of agent does not work for MI5

Impresario A person who puts on shows he hopes will make a big impression.

Makeup artist This is someone who puts make up on the performers before they go in front of an audience. It is not someone who draws pictures with lipstick.

Talent scout A person who looks for good performers. You will not impress a talent scout if you say 'Dib dib dib'. They are not that kind of scout.

Wardrobe The place in a theatre or film studio where the costumes are kept – not the secret way into Narnia.

Mystery Mob

Mystery Mob Set 1:

Mystery Mob and the Abominable Snowman
Mystery Mob and the Big Match
Mystery Mob and the Circus of Doom
Mystery Mob and the Creepy Castle
Mystery Mob and the Haunted Attic
Mystery Mob and the Hidden Treasure
Mystery Mob and the Magic Bottle
Mystery Mob and the Missing Millions
Mystery Mob and the Monster on the Moor
Mystery Mob and the Mummy's Curse
Mystery Mob and the Time Machine
Mystery Mob and the UFO

Mystery Mob Set 2:

Mystery Mob and the Ghost Town
Mystery Mob and the Bonfire Night Plot
Mystery Mob and the April Fools' Day Joker
Mystery Mob and the Great Pancake Day Race
Mystery Mob and the Scary Santa
Mystery Mob and the Conker Conspiracy
Mystery Mob and the Top Talent Contest
Mystery Mob and the Night in the Waxworks
Mystery Mob and the Runaway Train
Mystery Mob and the Wrong Robot
Mystery Mob and the Day of the Dinosaurs
Mystery Mob and the Man-eating Tiger

RISING ★ STARS

Mystery Mob books are available from most booksellers.

**For mail order information
please call Rising Stars on 0871 47 23 010
or visit www.risingstars-uk.com**